D1620900

re-told by
Philip Page

Published in association with
The Basic Skills Agency

Hodder & Stoughton

A MEMBER OF THE HODDER

Acknowledgements
Cover: Doug Lewis
Illustrations: Philip Page

Orders; please contact Bookpoint Ltd, 39 Milton Park, Abingdon, Oxon OX14
4TD. Telephone: (44) 01235 400414, Fax: (44) 01235 400454. Lines are open
from 9.00–6.00, Monday to Saturday, with a 24 hour message answering service.
Email address: orders@bookpoint.co.uk

British Library Cataloguing in Publication Data
A catalogue record for this title is available from the British Library

ISBN 0 340 77682 X

First published 2000
Impression number 10 9 8 7 6 5 4 3 2 1
Year   2005 2004 2003 2002 2001 2000

Copyright © 2000 Philip Page

Typeset by GreenGate Publishing Services, Tonbridge, Kent.
Printed in Great Britain for Hodder and Stoughton Educational, a division of
Hodder Headline Plc, 338 Euston Road, London NW1 3BH, by Atheneum
Press, Gateshead, Tyne & Wear

The Odyssey

Contents

About the Story

Odysseus (**Oh-dis-ee-uss**) is a Greek king.
'The Odyssey' is the story of a journey he makes.
It takes him ten years!

He leaves Troy after fighting a war there.
He wants to go home to the island of Ithaca.
He wants to see his wife Penelope (**Pen-el-oh-pee**)
and his son Telemachus (**Tel-em-ak-uss**) again.

On his journey he has many adventures.
A giant called Polyphemus (**Poll-if-ee-mus**) with
one eye tries to kill him.
Circe (**Sir-say**), a witch, tries to turn him into a pig.
A monster called Scylla (**Skil-a**) nearly eats him.
He becomes the only human to hear the Sirens
(**Sy-rens**) sing and live!
A beautiful woman called Calypso (**Kal-ip-so**)
falls in love with him.

Finally Odysseus arrives home.
Nobody recognises him.
He has to think of a plan to win back his Queen.

1

Odysseus Leaves Troy

The war between the Greeks and the Trojans
was over.
It had lasted for 10 years.
Now the city of Troy lay in ruins.
Its palaces were ruined.
Its houses were burnt.
Its walls had been pulled down.
Its people had been put to death.

Odysseus was a Greek leader.
Now he wanted to go home
to the island of Ithaca.
He wanted to see his wife, Penelope, again.
He and his soldiers went to their ships
and set sail from Troy.

Odysseus had not wanted to go to Troy.
A fortune-teller had said that if he did,
he would not come home for 20 years.
He hoped the fortune-teller was wrong.

Odysseus and his men
pulled up the great square sails on their ships.
Soon the smoking ruins of Troy were far
behind.

Then a great storm blew up.
It lasted for days.
It blew the ships towards the coast of Africa.

All the men were glad when they saw land at last.
Odysseus sent some of his men ashore.
They went to look for food and fresh water.
When they did not return he went to look
for them.

They were with the people of that land.
The people were called the Lotos-eaters.
Odysseus's men had been given a strange fruit
to eat.
It was called the Lotos plant.
People who ate it forgot who they were and
where they came from.

The Lotos-eaters offered the fruit to Odysseus.
He refused.
He dragged his men back to the ships
and set sail.

2

The Cyclops

It was not long before they reached
another island.
This time Odysseus led his men ashore.
They looked around but could not see anyone.

They began to explore the island.
Soon they found a great cave.
Inside they found goats in a wooden pen.
There were great cheeses
hanging in baskets on the walls.

Odysseus and his men killed some goats and
roasted them.
They helped themselves to some of the cheese.

Later in the day the creature that lived in
the cave came back.
He was a Cyclops – a giant who had only
one eye in the middle of his forehead.
He drove a flock of sheep into the cave.
Then he rolled a great stone across the entrance.

'Who are you?' roared the Cyclops.

'We are travellers,' said Odysseus.
'We want only food and shelter
before we go on our way.'

For an answer the Cyclops picked up two of
Odysseus's men.
He killed them and ate them.

In the morning the Cyclops ate two more men.
He rolled back the great stone and
drove out the sheep.

Then he put the stone back.
Odysseus and his men were trapped.
The stone was too big for them to move.

When the giant came back
he killed another two men.
Odysseus knew he had to escape
as soon as possible.
He thought of a plan.

He and his men had brought some
strong wine with them.
He gave it to the Cyclops.

'What is your name?' Odysseus asked.
'My name is Polyphemus,' said the Cyclops
while he was drinking. 'What is yours?'
'My name is No-man,' Odysseus replied.
'I will eat you last,' said Polyphemus.

Soon the Cyclops fell into a drunken sleep.
Odysseus found a long pole.
He sharpened one end into a point.
Then he hardened the point in the fire.

Slowly he moved to where
the Cyclops was sleeping.
Then, with all his strength he stabbed the pole
into the one eye of the giant.

The Cyclops was blinded.
He screamed in pain.
He staggered through the cave
trying to catch the Greeks.
Odysseus and his men were able to dodge him.
But they could not escape
because of the great stone.

9

Some other Cyclops heard his screams.
They came to see what the trouble was.
'Who has done this to you?' they asked.
'No-man did this to me,' Polyphemus replied.
The other Cyclops laughed and went away.

In the morning the Cyclops pushed back
the stone.
Then he sat at the entrance.
Odysseus tied each of his men under a sheep.
The Cyclops felt the backs of the sheep
as they went out of the cave.
Odysseus clung to the underside
of the last sheep.
That was how they escaped.

3

Odysseus and Circe

Now Odysseus sailed north.
Soon he came to the island
of the Keeper of the Winds.

The Greeks stayed there for over a month.
When it was time for them to leave,
the Keeper of the Winds gave them
a leather bag.
It was tied with a silver wire.

'In here are winds,' he said.
'If you need them, use them carefully
to get you home.'

Odysseus thanked him and set sail.

Their ships had almost reached Ithaca when
Odysseus fell asleep.
His men thought there might be wine
in the leather bag.
They untied the silver wire.

At once the winds escaped.
They blew the ships far away from Ithaca.
The winds scattered the ships.
Only Odysseus's ship survived.

Once again, Odysseus and his men found
themselves on the shore of a strange land.

Odysseus sent some men to explore.
They saw an amazing sight!
They found a palace surrounded by wild animals.
But these fierce animals were as gentle as pets!

A beautiful woman came out of the palace.
She invited them inside.
She gave them food and wine.
The woman's name was Circe.
The Greeks did not know that she was a witch.
She cast a spell on the men and
turned them into pigs.

One man escaped and went back
to tell Odysseus.
Odysseus had heard of Circe.
He knew how to resist her spells.
The scent of a special flower would protect him.

He found the flower and held it tightly.
Circe welcomed him.
She gave him food and drink.
Then she tried to cast her spell on him.

Odysseus quickly sniffed the flower.
The spell did not work.
He drew his sword.

'Turn all these animals back into men,'
he said to Circe.
'If you don't, I will kill you.'

Circe agreed.
She touched each animal with her magic wand.
The animals were turned back into men.

For two years Odysseus stayed with Circe.
Then he said it was time to set sail again.

Circe did not want him to leave.
'If you must go,' she said.
'I cannot stop you. But take care.
There are many dangers ahead of you.'

4

The Sirens

Odysseus soon found out what the dangers were!
He had to sail between a great whirlpool and
a terrible monster called Scylla.
The monster had six heads and ate human flesh.

Odysseus tried to avoid the whirlpool.
But he sailed too close to Scylla.
It picked up six of his men and ate them.

Circe had also warned him about the Sirens.

NEWCASTLE-UNDER-LYME
COLLEGE LEARNING
17 RESOURCES

The Sirens had the heads of girls and
the bodies of birds.
Anybody who heard their beautiful singing
fell under a spell.
They could not leave and they starved to death.

Odysseus wanted to hear the song of
the Sirens.
He put wax in the ears of his men
so they could not hear them.
Then they tied him to the ship's mast.

They sailed close to the land of the Sirens.
Odysseus heard their song.
It was the most beautiful sound he had ever
heard.
He shouted to his men to untie him.
He threatened to kill them all
if they did not free him.
But they could not hear him.

The ship sailed on past the Sirens.
Odysseus was the only person to hear them
and live!

5

Odysseus and Calypso

While they were at sea there was another storm.
Lightning hit the ship and it sank.

All the men drowned except for Odysseus.
He clung to some wreckage and was saved.

Half drowned,
Odysseus was washed up on a beach.
There, a young woman called Calypso found him.

Calypso fell in love with Odysseus.
She nursed him until he was better.
She asked him to stay with her.

'If you stay with me,' Calypso said,
'you will live for ever and you will never grow old.'

Odysseus stayed with Calypso
for more than five years.
But he became more and more homesick.
For hours and hours he sat on the cliffs by
the sea staring at the horizon.

'Why do you sit here, day after day?'
Calypso asked him.
'I want to go home,' said Odysseus.
'I have a wife and a son in Ithaca.
I have not seen them for nearly 20 years.'

Calypso was sad, but she helped Odysseus
to build a raft of logs.
She gave him food and water for his voyage.

Odysseus kissed her and thanked her.
Then he set sail for Ithaca

6

The Homecoming of Odysseus

After 20 years, Odysseus arrived
at his home land of Ithaca.

Nobody recognised him.
Servants would not let him enter the palace.
He was old, dirty and dressed in rags.
They thought he was a beggar.
He did not look anything like the King
who had gone away to war.

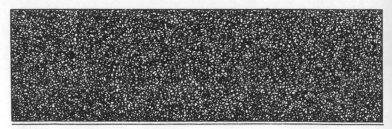

24

Only his old dog knew him.
It limped up to him wagging its tail.
Odysseus stroked it.
The dog licked its master's hand and died.

Odysseus's son was called Telemachus.
He had been away from Ithaca.
He had been trying to find news of his father
after the end of the war against Troy.

When he came back he met Odysseus.
He did not know who he was at first.
Then Odysseus told Telemachus
stories of his childhood.
Only his father would have known those stories.

'It is good that you have come back, father,'
said Telemachus.
'Everybody thinks you are dead.'

'What has happened to your mother?'
Odysseus asked.
'She has waited for you,' replied Telemachus.
'But there are many men here
who want to marry her.'

'Take me into the palace,' said Odysseus.

Inside the palace he saw all the men.
They behaved as though the palace was
their own.

When they saw Odysseus in his rags
they insulted him.
'Get rid of this beggar,' they said.

The next day the men told Penelope that
she must choose one of them to marry.
Penelope said she did not know how to choose.

Odysseus had a plan.
He told it to Telemachus.

Telemachus told Penelope to say she would
marry the man who could draw Odysseus's bow.

Telemachus and his servants hid
all the men's weapons.
Then they locked the doors of the palace.

One by one the men tried to draw the bow.
None of them could.

Odysseus picked up the bow.
He drew it easily.
He shot an arrow through the throat
of one of the men.

At once all the others knew
who the beggar in rags really was.
They tried to escape
but the doors were locked.
They looked for their swords and shields
but they had been hidden.

Odysseus killed them all.

At last he was reunited with his wife and son.
After 20 years he had come home.
It was just as the fortune teller had said.